THIS BOOK
BELONGS TO

....

MW00887092

LOOK OUT FOR MORE POOP-TASTIC BOOKS IN THIS RANGE:

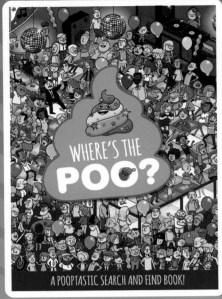

A POOPTASTIC SEARCH AND FIND BOOK!

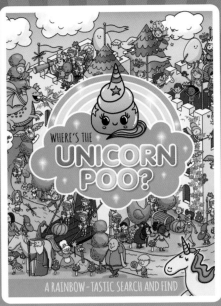

A RAINBOW-TASTIC SEARCH AND FIND

A DINO-TASTIC SEARCH AND FIND

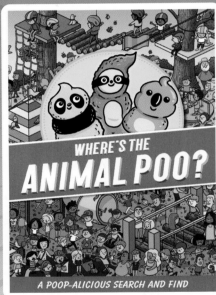

A POOP-ALICIOUS SEARCH AND FIND

A SPOOKTACULAR SEARCH AND FIND

A POO-PACKED SEARCH AND FIND

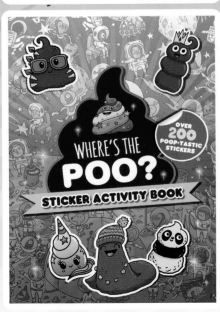

ON YOUR MARKS, GET SET, SEARCH!

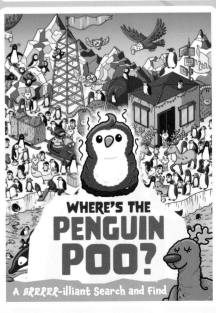

A BRRRRR-illiant Search and Find

WHERE'S THE
PIRATE POO?

ORCHARD

MEET THE POOS

Ahoy, Matey! Our pirate poo crew have come up to the poop deck to say hello. They're about to set sail on a swashbuckling adventure. Can you find them in every scene?

CAPTAIN QUEENIE

The leader of the crew. Don't get on her wrong side, or she'll make you walk the plank . . . Plop!

SALTY

The chef poo loves cooking up a storm. All the pirate poos love his gruel!

BEACH BUMS

Land, ho! The pirate poos have washed up on a busy beach. Can you find them hiding among the sunbathers and swimmers?

DANCING QUEENIE

Top of the Poops! Can you spot Queenie and the rest of her crew shaking their pirate booties at the disco?

PIRATE MAYHEM

On guard! The pirates are practising their sword skills. You might need a telescope to spot the poos hiding among the pirate gear.

ODD ONE OUT!
Can you spot the telescope, cutlass and hat that look different to the others?

SLIPPERY SLIDES

The pirate poos love shooting down the pipes at the water park. Can you find Duckie and his shipmates bobbing about in the water?

SCHOOL MATES

Ahoy, class-matey! Believe it or not, even pirate poos go to school. Can you spot Bluebeard and the other poos in this classroom?

PIRATE BOOTY

The poos have found a hidden treasure chest! Can you see them hiding among the jewels and gold coins?

ODD ONE OUT!

Can you spot the coin, gem and goblet that look different from the rest?

SEA SHANTIES

Yo-ho-ho! It's time for a sea shanty! The pirate poos are having fun at this music festival, but where are they hiding in the crowd?

FISH FRENZY

Captain Queenie has made the pirate poos walk the plank and go for a swim. Can you find all the poos before they get gobbled up by the sea monsters?

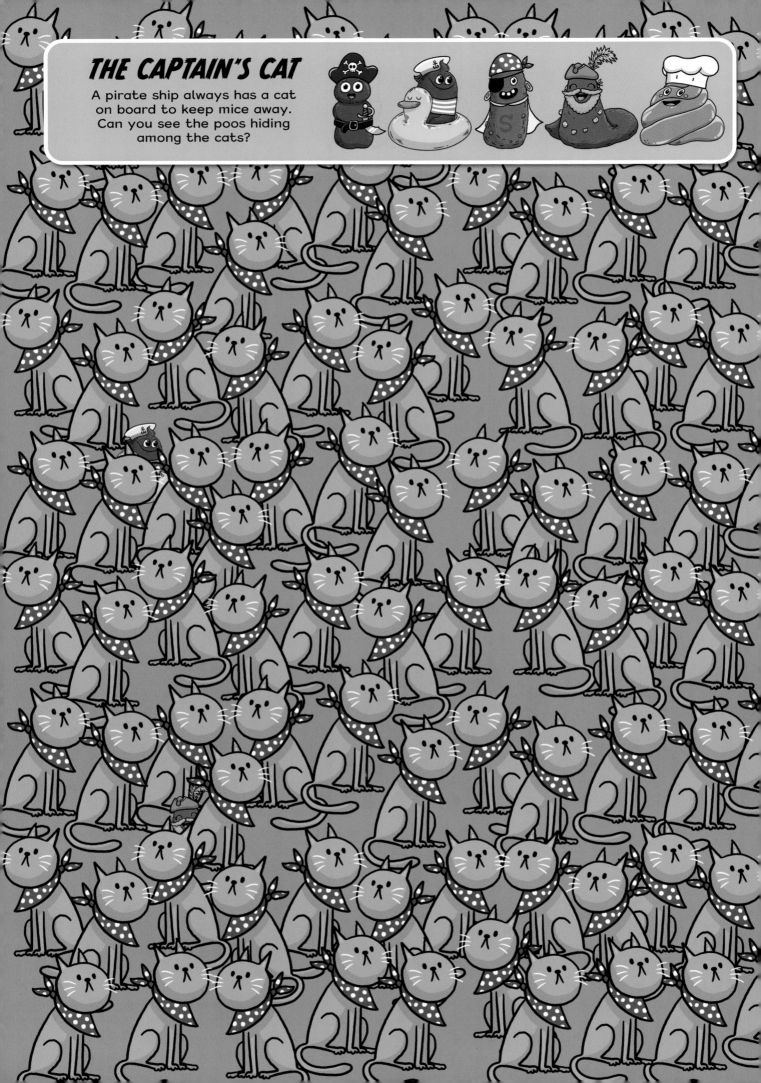

THE CAPTAIN'S CAT

A pirate ship always has a cat on board to keep mice away. Can you see the poos hiding among the cats?

ODD ONE OUT!

The captain's cat looks slightly different to the rest – can you spot her?

MUMMY MUSEUM

The pirate poos always visit the local sights when they dock at a new port. Can you find Superpoo and his shipmates at the mummy museum?

SHIVERY SNACKS

Shiver me timbers, it's cold in here! Salty and his friends have stopped by for a refreshing snack. Can you find them in the ice cream parlour?

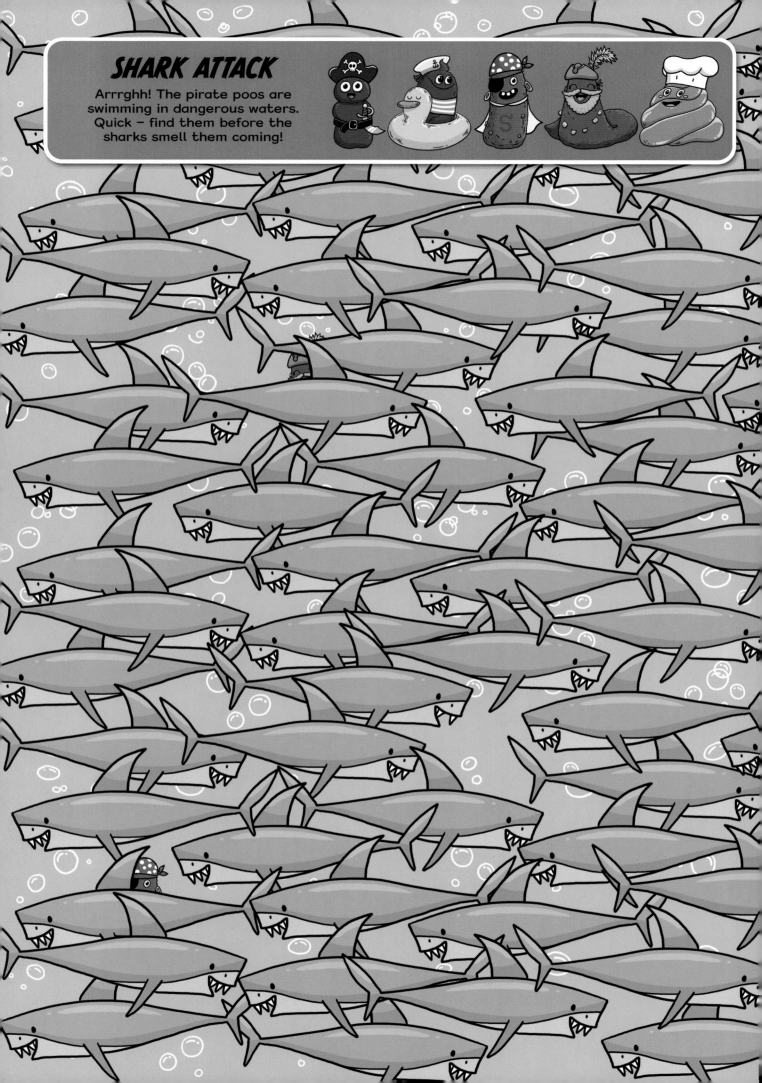

SHARK ATTACK

Arrrghh! The pirate poos are swimming in dangerous waters. Quick – find them before the sharks smell them coming!

SKELETON CREW

Bluebeard and his buccaneering crew are marooned in this haunted house. Can you find them hiding among the spooky scallywags?

ANCHORS AWAY!

Captain Queenie is ready to set sail! But wait, not all the poos are on board . . . Can you find them before the ship leaves the island?

ANSWERS

Now try and find the extra items hidden in each scene.

BEACH BUMS

Seven palm trees ☐

A shark fin ☐

A blue guitar ☐

Three doughnut floats ☐

A man with two ice creams ☐

A big red lobster ☐

An anchor ☐

Two crabs ☐

Seven seagulls ☐

An octopus ☐

DANCING QUEENIE

Four disco balls ☐

Six red balloons ☐

Two boys with blue hair ☐

A white t-shirt with a red stripe ☐

Nine bow ties ☐

Three purple drinks ☐

A dinosaur t-shirt ☐

A man in dungarees ☐

A red cap ☐

Four green stars ☐

PIRATE MAYHEM

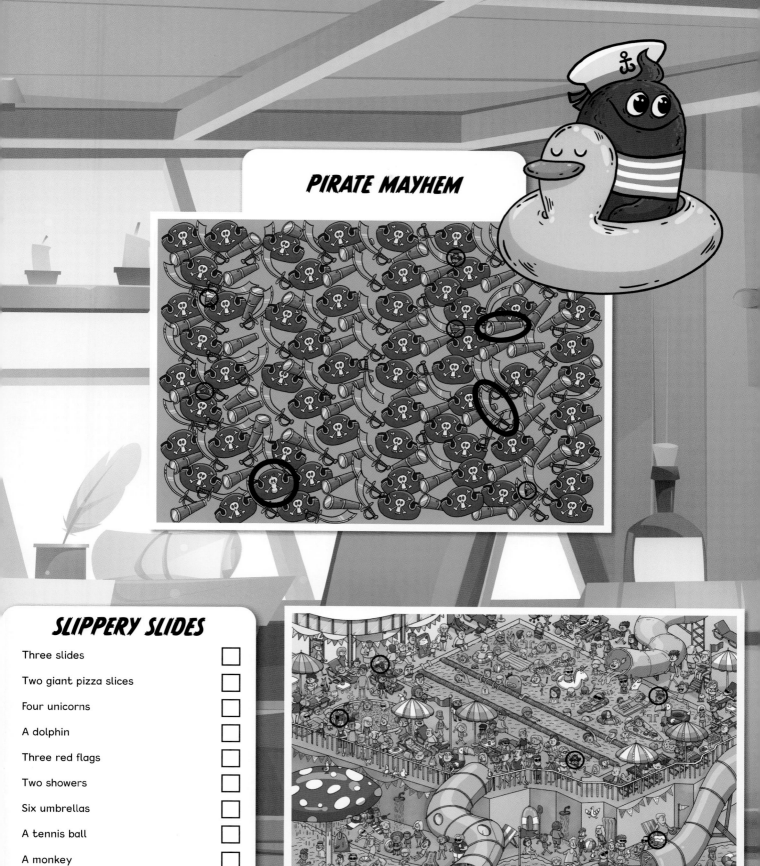

SLIPPERY SLIDES

Three slides ☐

Two giant pizza slices ☐

Four unicorns ☐

A dolphin ☐

Three red flags ☐

Two showers ☐

Six umbrellas ☐

A tennis ball ☐

A monkey ☐

Eleven birds ☐

SCHOOL MATES

- A clock ☐
- A globe ☐
- Four easels ☐
- Six handprints ☐
- Eight paper towel rolls ☐
- Two bean bags ☐
- A pigeon ☐
- A pink mug ☐
- Ten pencil cases ☐
- Six glue sticks ☐

PIRATE BOOTY

SEA SHANTIES

Seven panda balloons ☐

A keyboard ☐

A clown ☐

A banjo ☐

A hula hoop ☐

Ten bales of hay ☐

A violin ☐

Four drums ☐

Four bananas ☐

Two kids with tiger face paint ☐

FISH FRENZY

Six lantern fish ☐

Four grey eels ☐

A fish with four stripes ☐

Three green octopuses ☐

Eleven pufferfish ☐

An orange coral with yellow stripes ☐

Seven shells ☐

Eleven pink jellyfish ☐

A sea monster with eleven teeth ☐

Two pink corals ☐

THE CAPTAIN'S CAT

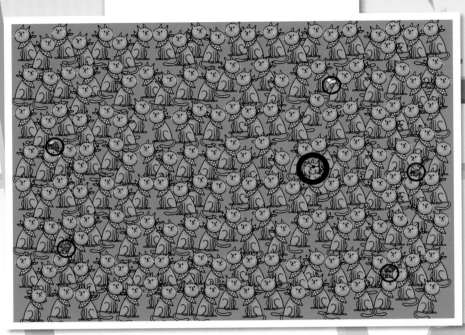

MUMMY MUSEUM

Two red snakes ☐

Three mummy dogs ☐

Five mice ☐

Two pyramids ☐

A cup of tea ☐

A couple taking a selfie ☐

A skull ☐

Five pillars ☐

A falling vase ☐

A red drink can ☐

SHIVERY SNACKS

- Eight napkin dispensers ☐
- Thirteen menus ☐
- Two mice ☐
- Four red chairs ☐
- Two yellow tables ☐
- A hat with a blue stripe ☐
- Four pink doughnuts ☐
- Six banana splits ☐
- A paper airplane ☐
- Sixteen cherries ☐

SHARK ATTACK

Did you find me? If you're stuck, try visiting the Slippery Slides again.

SKELETON CREW

Eleven pumpkins ☐

Four ghosts ☐

A tube of toothpaste ☐

Twenty-seven tombstones ☐

A candle ☐

A jar of eyeballs ☐

Eight trees ☐

A flying vampire ☐

A clown ☐

Four pairs of devil horns ☐

ANCHORS AWAY!

Five barrels ☐

A skull-and-crossbones flag ☐

Two anchors ☐

A treasure chest ☐

Two gold goblets ☐

A treasure map ☐

Three pink gems ☐

A pearl necklace ☐

Six pirate hats ☐

Four crabs ☐

ORCHARD BOOKS
First published in Great Britain in 2022 by The Watts Publishing Group © 2022 The Watts Publishing Group Limited
Illustrations by Dynamo Limited   Additional images © Shutterstock
A CIP catalogue record for this book is available from the British Library
ISBN 978 1 40836 690 5   Printed and bound in China   3 5 7 9 10 8 6 4 2

Orchard Books, an imprint of Hachette Children's Group
Part of The Watts Publishing Group Limited, Carmelite House, 50 Victoria Embankment, London, EC4Y 0DZ
An Hachette UK Company   www.hachette.co.uk   www.hachettechildrens.co.uk

FSC

MIX
Paper from responsible sources
FSC® C104740